LETS HIMSELF GO

DIK BROWNE

ATTICA
PUBLICATIONS
ATTICA PUBLICATIONS ENGLAND

This edition published by
Attica Publications 1985

Attica Publications
A Division of Argus Communications
DLM House, Edinburgh Way,
Harlow, Essex CM20 2HL, England.

ISBN 1 85176 009 1

HÄGAR The Horrible

by DIK BROWNE

12-7

DIK BROWNE

HÄGAR The Horrible
by DIK BROWNE

MAMA SAYS THE TIME HAS COME FOR ME TO HAVE A TALK WITH YOU.

ABOUT WHAT?

HOW I SHOULD GO ABOUT PICKING A MATE...

OH! I CAN TELL YOU THAT!

MY SON, IN CHOOSING A MATE THERE ARE *THREE* THINGS YOU SHOULD LOOK FOR...

FIRST—STRENGTH—THAT'S THE MOST IMPORTANT THING! BIG, FAT MUSCLES!!

AND *HAIR*—LOTTSA HAIR—ALL OVER THE LEGS AND ARMS!

AND SHARP TEETH... NOT MANY, BUT SHARP LIKE DAGGERS!!

HEY! WHERE ARE YOU GOING?!!

I DIDN'T TELL YOU HOW TO PICK THE REST OF THE CREW!

5-9
DIK BROWNE

HÄGAR The Horrible

by DIK BROWNE

HÄGAR The Horrible

by DIK BROWNE

OUR LAND IS VERY BEAUTIFUL, ISN'T IT, DAD?

YES, MY SON. BUT IT IS MORE THAN THAT.

IT GIVES US EVERYTHING WE NEED FOR THE GOOD LIFE... TREES FOR BUILDING... BERRIES FOR EATING... ROCKS FOR THROWING...

LOOK, DAD! A STRANGER IS FISHING IN OUR POND!

NOW, NOW...

IT ISN'T *OUR* POND... THE GODS WHO MADE PONDS MADE THEM FOR ALL MEN TO SHARE.

THE SAME AS THE SUN, THE STARS AND THE MOON AND THE SOFT EVENING BREEZE ... DO YOU UNDERSTAND?

AND BESIDES... THERE ARE NO FISH IN THAT POND...

LOOK!

I GOT ONE!

DIK BROWNE
11-23

STOP FISHING IN MY POND!!

HÄGAR The Horrible

by Dik BROWNE

MY! THE 6:15 FROM OSLO IS LATE TONIGHT...

HAGAR DOES PUT IN A LONG DAY — POOR DEAR...

OH, DEAR, HAGAR LOOKS SO BEAT! HE IS WORKING TOO HARD! I SHOULD BE NICER TO HIM...

♪ DARLING ♪ YOU'RE HOME ♪

YOU REST THOSE POOR TIRED FEET IN THIS EASY CHAIR.

A LITTLE LIBATION WILL HELP UNRAVEL THOSE OLD NERVES.

NOW, YOU SIT THERE AND RELAX AND I'LL GET YOU A REAL NICE DINNER.

1-25
DIK BROWNE

WHAT A DAY!! FIRST I LOSE THE BATTLE...THEN THE BOOTY...I GET ZAPPED SIX TIMES...FINALLY MAKE IT HOME, ONLY TO FIND THAT MY WIFE HAS GONE NUTS!

HÄGAR The Horrible

by DIK BROWNE

HÄGAR The Horrible

by DIK BROWNE

HOW AM I, DOCTOR?

NOT BAD FOR THE SHAPE YOU'RE IN...

BUT GIVE ME A MINUTE— I'LL FIND SOMETHING.

WHAT'S THIS FOR, DR. ZOOK?

IT'S TO WARD OFF IMPS, DEMONS AND EVIL SPIRITS.

THERE'S A LOT OF IT GOING AROUND.

BUT DIDN'T I GET THIS ALREADY?

YES, YOU DID...

AWK!

OOK!

SWAK!

YOU JUST NEEDED A BOOSTER.

DIK BROWNE

1-11

HÄGAR The Horrible

by DiK BROWNE

HÄGAR The Horrible
by Dik BROWNE

HÄGAR The Horrible

by DIK BROWNE

HÄGAR The Horrible

by DIK BROWNE

HÄGAR The Horrible
by DIK BROWNE

HÄGAR The Horrible

by DIK BROWNE

IT BEGAN, A MERE TICKLE, IN HAGAR'S TOES
TURNED TO A SNIFFLE
AND SLOWLY IT ROSE...

HE KNEW AT ONCE THIS WAS NO TRIFLE
AND TRY AS HE MIGHT HE NEVER WOULD STIFLE...

...THE GREAT SNEEZE

EGAD! HAGAR IS GOING TO SNEEZE!

AH-AH...

RUN FOR YOUR LIFE!

...CHOO

THAT WAS THE START OF THE WORLD'S GREATEST SNEEZE

IT TOPPLED BIG CHIMNEYS AND UPROOTED TREES

IT WAS FELT IN ASIA AND KENSINGTON, TOO
AND EVEN ON THE OCEAN BLUE

AND IT FINALLY MADE A PALM TREE SWAY
IN BOONA-BOONA FAR AWAY

1-18

AND MOVED A NATIVE WIFE TO SAY:

NOW WHERE DID YOU CATCH THAT?!

ACHOO

DIK BROWNE

HÄGAR The Horrible

by DIK BROWNE

12-14

HÄGAR The Horrible
by Dik Browne

DANCES TODAY ARE CRAZY

YOU'D NEVER CATCH ME DANCING LIKE THAT

I KNOW...

YEAH! 'RAY!

'RAY!

MY FOOT WAS ASLEEP

DIK BROWNE — 4-25

HÄGAR The Horrible

by Dik Browne

HÄGAR The Horrible

by Dik Browne

HÄGAR The Horrible

by DIK BROWNE

HÄGAR The Horrible

by Dik Browne

YOU KNOW WHAT'S WRONG WITH MY WIFE? I'LL TELL YOU—

SHE NEVER LISTENS TO ME...NO MATTER WHAT I SAY, SHE GOES RIGHT AHEAD AND...

...YOU SEE, THE TROUBLE IS— MY WIFE DOESN'T UNDERSTAND ME... I'M JUST THE GUY THAT BRINGS HOME THE LOOT...

...BOY! THE THINGS I COULD TELL YOU...I COULD HAVE BEEN A REAL BIG SHOT...LET ME TELL YOU...

...AND THEN ON THE OTHER HAND, I ASK YOU—WHAT'S IT ALL ABOUT? I MEAN LIFE...DID YOU EVER THINK OF THAT...

IT SURE IS SWEET OF YOU TO LISTEN LIKE THIS, GIRLIE... I WISH...

TIME TO CLOSE UP, EMMA.

EMMA! TIME TO CLOSE UP!

DIK BROWNE 1-4

SORRY, CHARLIE...WHEN I'M WEARING THESE EAR PLUGS I CAN'T HEAR A THING...

HÄGAR The Horrible

by DIK BROWNE

HÄGAR The Horrible
by DIK BROWNE

© King Features Syndicate, Inc., 1976. World rights reserved.

DIK BROWNE — 7-11

HÄGAR The Horrible

by Dik Browne

OKAY, FELLAS, WE'LL SKIP THE TREASURER'S REPORT.

THAT ENDS THE BUSINESS PART OF THIS MEETING

AND NOW, A LITTLE ENTERTAINMENT FROM KNUTE THE NUT!

HI THERE, LADIES AND GERMS—I GOT A KINDA CUTE ETHNIC JOKE FOR YOU...

© King Features Syndicate, Inc., 1976. World rights reserved

BUT FIRST—ARE THERE ANY BURGUNDIANS PRESENT?

NO?? GOOD!

NO USE HURTING FEELINGS... WELL, YOU ALL KNOW HOW SLOW BURGUNDIANS ARE—RIGHT? SO THERE WAS THIS GUY FROM BURGUNDY AND HE WANTED TO PEEL A FIG...

DIK BROWNE

SO HE SAYS TO HIS WIFE: "HOW DO YOU PEEL A FIG?" AND HIS WIFE, WHO IS AS SLOW AS HE IS, SAYS: "I'LL ASK MY..."

HEY... WAIT A MINUTE... I'M A BURGUNDIAN!

2-22

HÄGAR The Horrible

by DIK BROWNE

DIK BROWNE - 3-28

HÄGAR The Horrible

by DIK BROWNE

BOY, AM I HUNGRY

THAT LOOKS LIKE A PLACE TO EAT

IS THIS A RESTAURANT?

IF IT ISN'T, THIS GUY IS SELLING TABLES

HOW CAN WE ORDER? WE DON'T SPEAK THEIR LINGO

EASY— WATCH

CLUCK! CLUCK! CLUCK!

AH, HA! BUNO!

HEY! TWO SCRAMBLED EGGS! THAT'S GREAT!

CLUCK! CLUCK! CLUCK!

DUOS ENTRES DAS OVO!

DIK BROWNE 7-25

HÄGAR The Horrible

by DIK BROWNE

8-1

ATTICA PUBLICATIONS ENGLAND